2 AM

100 Things You

DARA LY

Table of Contents

Legal Notice

The author has strived to be as accurate and complete as possible in the creation of this book, notwithstanding the fact that he does not warrant or represent at any time that the contents within are perfectly accurate due to the rapidly changing nature of information transformation.

Although all attempts have been made to verify information provided in this book, the author assumes no responsibility for errors, omissions, or contrary interpretation of the subject matter herein.

Any perceived slights of specific persons, people, or organizations are unintentional.

In practical advice books, like anything else in life, there are no guarantees. Thus, readers are cautioned to rely on their own judgment about their individual circumstances to act accordingly.

This book is not intended for use as a source of professional advice. The readers are advised to seek services of competent professionals in the fields.

Acknowledgements

First of all, I'd like to thank my editor Sovanchanbomey Chith. With your great patience in editing, this book is made possible. We made it, at last. Thank God!

I also want to thank my illustrator Champey Ouk for a beautiful book cover design.

I want to thank two special people SreyNak Sorn and Panha Sok for allowing me to rewrite their stories and add into this book. Undoubtedly, their stories are motivational and interesting. I am forever grateful for their kindness. Moreover, I want to express my gratitude toward other fans too even though I couldn't mention all of them due to the fact that there are too many names to count here. Let's just say I'm too lazy to count.

Last but not least, I'd like to thank *D2D Print* for publishing this book. Thank you for your great service.

Dedicated to DARA LY Books Fans!

About the Author

DARA LY is the graduate from the University of Puthisastra (UP), bachelor degree of English Literature. He's the Chairman of DARA LY Books, a small book publishing group serving the readers on the topics, such as education, inspiration, and entertainment.

As a lifelong reader, he has founded **DARA LY Reading Space** to open the study clubs for the young generation of Cambodia. He is determined to keep his clubs free of charge, as always.

Since September 5, 2016, Dara Ly has published 15 books, all are for teenagers in Cambodia. His goal is simple (and he's silly enough to pursue it). He wants to encourage young Cambodian people to read 50 books a year.

Introduction

I wrote this book at 2 AM because I couldn't sleep. The reason? Heartbreak. It was so depressing that I could not find peace in my mind. It was a difficult time anybody could face. I decided to write down what I was thinking. Boy, did I write a lot. Indeed, most stories from this book were authentic and sad. The funny thing was that I could heal my heartbreak after I had finished writing this book.

At first, I didn't think I would publish this book. Believe me, some stories were very depressing. Nobody would want to learn or experience such things. Along the way, I had learned something crucial about this book and myself too. To find out more, you will have to read by yourself. Okay?

Anyway, I would like to remind you that this book "**2AM**" was written by a heartbroken person (Dara Ly the Human), and mainly, it's for heartbroken people, so it is logical that most messages are being sent to people who need motivation.

Please read this book to find out more.

Do not take it personally.

Read more to understand about yourself.

This book is your friend.

Good luck, **My Reader!**

PART 1
2AM

DARA LY

1

The Third Type

There are two types of people in this world. Type one and type two. And there is the third type. The type of person who can never escape from heartbreak. I am the third type.

There are two types of relationships. Type one and type two. And there is the third type. The type of relationship which will break your heart. I have suffered from that type of relationship.

There are two types of men. Type one and type two. And there is the third type. The type of man who breaks my heart. I am attracted to that type of man.

There are two types of late-night owls. Type one and type two. And there is the third type. The type of person who can't sleep at night. Now it's 2 AM, and I am still here, so I am the third type of late-night owl.

There are many things in my mind, but I can't tell anyone. Clearly, I can't tell him because he's gone. He doesn't care about me. I told him that I'll be fine, but I'm not really sure if I'll be okay. What am I going to do?

2

Why?

I am not strong enough to accept what happened. I lie to myself, thinking that nothing bad happened between us. I pretend that you're still here with me.

Sorry for falling in love with you. It was a mistake. Sorry for being a toxic girl. I was a bad girl. Sorry for making your life miserable. It was my fault.

Still, I want to tell you that love is about giving, not taking. I'm willing to let you go if it makes you happy. I'm willing to give you that happiness if that is what you want. I'm willing to do that even if it breaks my heart.

I am trying so hard to forget everything that you did to me and omit you from my memory, but I cannot do that. My tears drop down ceaselessly whenever I think about you.

How long do I have to endure this nightmare? Why can't you keep your promise? Why did you leave me?

Can you tell me why?

3

Hurtful

It is hurtful when you love someone who loves someone else; I understand how it feels. It is very hurtful when someone takes you for granted; I know what it's like. It is beyond hurtful when someone breaks your heart and destroys your trust; I have experienced that. It is hurtful.

People choose to give up on a relationship because of these reasons. They don't want to deal with jealousy, fear of rejection, and heartbreak. To them, love is only a fairy tale, barely real from the beginning, hurtful in the process, and really painful at the end.

I gave my heart to him, and he broke it into pieces. He took my happiness away, and he left me alone in a dark place. There's nothing left.

I tried to make this relationship work, but he made sure it would fail. He succeeded. He never cared about me. He never wanted to be with me. He just wanted to win the game, and he thought I was a trophy. When he's tired of me, he threw me away. It is hurtful.

4

Mistake

Falling in love with you was the first mistake. Accepting you was the second mistake. Asking you to stay was the third mistake.

I shouldn't have fallen in love with you. I should have listened to my friends. They were right about you. I was not the only one whom you loved. In fact, I was just a temporary person. I should have known that since the beginning.

We were supposed to be just friends. We were not supposed to fall in love with each other, but I was silly enough to believe that you could be a better person. I accepted you because I thought you could protect my heart. I was wrong. Even though you hurt me, I still gave you a second chance. You never changed. You never wanted to make it work. You only came back to me because you had nobody else. It was a mistake for letting you come back to ruin my peace once more. I was stupid enough to let you fool me over and over again.

5

Regret

I regret that I loved you. I should have focused on my study instead of wasting my time with this relationship. I would have been happier if I hadn't met you. My life would have been good if I had listened to myself. It was too late. It's over between us too.

It was never going to work between us. I should have known that earlier. I was so devoted to this relationship that I had never cared about myself. I sacrificed many things just to keep it, but I still failed. I failed to keep you in my life because you wanted to go.

Your love faded away when you ran away from me, but the wound in my heart was still there. It only got worse day by day. Nobody cared about me. I had to deal with this suffering alone.

What should I do with my life now? Can anybody tell me what to do?

2AM

6

It Did Happen

What a fool I was! I didn't see it coming. The fact that our relationship was a train wreck in slow motion.

Love between two people is an agreement honored by both sides. When one side tries to terminate the deal, things might turn out to be bad for the other one. That's what happened between us. You decided to end our love and walked away from this relationship. I'm the one who suffers the consequences, but I don't blame you.

Before I decided to confess to you, I knew someday you would hurt me, but I prayed that it wouldn't happen too soon. Well, it did happen. You did hurt me, a lot.

I tried to reason with myself even though my heart was aching. It hurt so much that I couldn't sleep. I couldn't eat. I couldn't do anything without thinking about you. It only hurt me more.

What should I do now?

(*It's 2 AM again!*)

7

Can We?

I take the pill hoping to get rid of my pain, but pain never goes away. It stays. Yes, it always does. What am I supposed to do now? Get rid of my pain or the memories of you?

Why can't you keep the promises? Why do you have to let me go? Why can't we try to find the solutions for this problem? We've got it worse, and yet we pulled it off because we stuck with each other. Why can't we stick to our commitment? Why?

I still couldn't figure out how our relationship had turned out to be like this. I always thought you loved me and wanted to be with me forever. Please tell me that I was right. Please tell me that you still love me. Please tell me that this is a dream.

Please don't let this nightmare destroy my life. It happened before, and it took me long enough to recover from the depression. Please don't let the same nightmare haunt me twice. We still can make things right.

Can we?

Painful

If you are reading this message right now, please stop reading it. Please do not continue reading it because it will only make your feelings unstable and unjustified. Your life is not about the past; it is about the present that you have, so you should learn to focus on the present and forget the past. Trust me, there is nothing good in it because it is just the past that slowly perishes through time. Let the time heal this wound. Forget me!

I am just a creature of habit, loving and hating and loving again and hating again. I am fueled by jealousy, and I always commit cruel things just to get revenge. I do not have a place in your heart, and you can never find true love in our relationship. Go now. You shall be free!

It's painful to let you go, but it's for your good. You won't find happiness trying to keep our relationship. It is over between us, and you should find a better person. I fail to keep my promises as I can't stay with you. You shall be happy without me, and you will have a good life. Please take care!

9

You're Gone

Every time you appear in my mind, it hurts me so much. It hurts because I know that I can't be with you anymore. It will hurt me even more when you find someone else. I don't know if I could face that situation.

Your smile was beautiful, and your eyes were purely innocent. I was a lucky person to be with you, but my luck had run out, and it's over between us. Good things have come to an end, but the best thing in my life is you. (It has always been you.)

However, I'm not the best person for you. I'm just the wound in your heart, so you don't have to feel sorry for me. Maybe I was the burden for you, so you decided to leave me. I'm just an unwanted experience in your life.

I decided to block you because I couldn't bear the fact that you would be with someone else but not me. I try to cut off from your world, hoping I could find peace. Sometimes your friends still send me your pictures, and it hurts me even more. It reminds me so much about our past and the good times that we used to have together. Now things change, you're gone, and I'm alone.

10

I'm Fine

You won't have to be sorry for my pain. You won't have to be sorry for my suffering. You won't have to be sorry for my own heartbreak. You don't need to feel sorry for anything. You owe me nothing. There is nothing to be sorry for.

I am not going to be sorry for myself either. I deserve that, and I accept my fate. Even though I can't bear the fact that you're gone, I must learn to accept it. Still, I want to tell you that I love you, and I always will. God knows I do.

However, I don't need sympathy from anybody, not even you. You don't have to feel guilty for leaving me. I won't do anything stupid. Don't worry. I'm fine.

I don't want to look like a victim of this breakup. Before I accepted you, I knew the consequences. I shall be fine. Although I'm alone, I will be okay. My life might not be the same again, I know, but I will learn to forget you. I will try to erase the memories from the past. I hope I can do that.

PART 2
Sadness

2AM

11

Unfair

That's a lonely feeling when you try everything you could to make someone happy, but she lets you down. Your effort goes in vain, but that's not the worst part.

The worst part is that you get accused of being such a disloyal one. It is unfair, but you have to live with it. You don't even get the chance to explain to her.

You lose faith in yourself when somebody loses trust in you. You become convinced that everything happens because of you. That's a sad feeling. It's unfair, but it's your life.

You accept it, and you don't even fight for yourself. You just let it be. You hide your misery. Now what? You want to find a new life? You can't have a new life unless and until you unlearn those unwanted thoughts. Most importantly, you have to erase the sad feeling.

When too many problems happen at the same time, it's hard to focus on the solutions. Your mind is busy dealing with bad things, and your feelings couldn't get worse. That's when you start to overthink.

12

I Will

You are the only thing that matters to me for my whole life. You are my one and only. I love you because you are you. I will wait until you come back to me. I will wait until you are ready to love once again. I will wait for you. I will.

A lot has happened this year, and my heart couldn't handle it, so I let it out last night. I cried like a baby last night because I was really in pain.

I don't want to break up, but he doesn't care about me, so I can't stop him. He wanted to leave. I asked him for the last time whether or not he wanted to stay, but he said no, so it's over now. Honestly, I don't want to let him go, but I have to.

I never thought a breakup would be hurtful. The least of all, I never thought he would break my heart this way. I'm disappointed, but I want to give him another chance too. I want to be with him again. Maybe it's just a wish!

2AM

13

Hurt You

Everything I do only hurts you. When I do something, it will hurt you. When I don't do anything, it still can hurt you. In short, I am the cause of every problem that you have.

I thought I could save this relationship, but I failed. You would be ashamed of me, seeing me the way I am, so I prefer not to let you see me in this situation. I want you to remember only the good things that we had. Just forget me because I was your worst nightmare.

I don't want to hurt you anymore, so you can go. I want you to have a happy life, and it's the life without me. Perhaps, you won't get hurt like you used to. It'll be a good life.

I want you to find someone else. Someone who can make you happy. Someone who will love you more than I could. Someone who won't break your heart like I did. Someone whom you love and can accept. Please have a good life!

14

Tired

I am tired of waiting. I am tired of overthinking. I am tired of scaring myself. I am tired of being a problem to you. I am tired of hoping and losing hope at the same time, but I am never tired of loving you. I want to let you know that I can wait for you.

The fear of losing you is so scary that I choose to wait. I know, it's a silly way to wait for someone who wants to go away forever, but I can't lose this last hope. It's a hope that might disappoint me, but I don't care.

No one knows what the future may bring because the future is uncertain, but I am certain that my will shall remain firm and unchanged. Maybe God is testing me. I am tired of everything except to wait for you, so I can wait, and I will wait.

I have all the time I need in the world, so it won't be a problem. But please do not stay away for too long. Come back to me, and we shall be happy together!

2AM

15
My Questions

Have you ever cared about my feelings? Have you ever thought that I've been hurt? I shed my tears because of you. Have you ever thought about that? Do you really think that I'm strong enough to handle it alone? Sorry, but I'm not. Some problems are just too much, and at times, I can be so weak that I could cry easily. One of the most difficult problems for me is a relationship. Right, I'm talking about us. I'm asking you to reconsider your decision! Could you do that for me? Maybe you won't do that for me. You think I will beg for your mercy. Are you very confident that I won't leave you?

I don't want to fight this alone. Why do you have to make me feel unloved and unwanted? Am I that useless? I want you to answer my questions, but I know you want to avoid me. I'm just an annoying person to you. I hate being like this, but I wish you would know that I'm in pain right now.

Could I have a normal relationship? Is it really hard for you to do that? Maybe I'm not important. That's why you do this to me.

16

Because I Was Stubborn

I never deserved you in the first place, and even a blind person could see it in a minute. Apparently, everything went wrong, unlike what we expected. I should accept it. Things could get worse if I stay. I never want to go, but I have no choice. Please forget me.

Because I was stubborn, I had ruined your life. A big part of it. I don't want to do that anymore. I should leave even though it's killing me inside.

Life is funny and unpredictable, and sometimes we have to pay the price. I guess this is the price of our love life. Breakup is the only solution although it breaks my heart to say this. We should break up.

I only hope you have a better life with the one who is better than me. I hope he won't hurt you like I did. Please take care.

Goodbye!

17

The Right One

I want to stop thinking about you. I want to stop waiting for your message, but I don't want to lose you. I hope one day you will know that you have always been the right one. I was blind that I didn't see you at first. It might be too late to realize, but in my mind, I always know whom I give my heart to. In my mind, there's only one person that matters to me the most. You are the one. I love you. I still do. You know that, don't you?

I miss you so much. I wish you would know that. I want to tell you that I still love you and miss you every day. I miss everything you said to me. You asked me if I got home yet. You reminded me about the shower. You wanted me to sleep early every night. I miss all of it. Do you miss it too? In fact, do you even miss me?

Since our breakup, you haven't texted me. It looks like you really want to leave. I still care about you. Do you know that? I always think of you. I just want to text you and tell you that I miss you so much, but we're just strangers now.

18

I Miss You

I miss you so much. I try to do a lot of things to keep myself busy so that I could forget you, but I never could. I miss you every day, and I want you to know my mind, but you will never know because we are too far from each other. From now on, I will try not to miss you; I hope it will work.

You will never text me first. I know I'm never going to get a sweet text like I used to. Where is your "*Good night*" text? What about your "*Good morning*" call? Why is it so hard just to text me? Are you that busy?

Too busy to text but free enough to hang out with your friends? Too busy to call me but free to chat with others?

I understand that I am not important anymore. In your eyes, I'm just another annoying person. I'm sorry about that. I will not disturb you from now on, so you can have a good life with others. You don't have to think about me because I am not important. I know that!

2AM

19

The Memories

The memories keep haunting me, day and night. And I hate that. I hate that so much. Just so much right now. Few memories are good, but many are cruel. I am like a small chicken running from place to place to hide, and hoping the storm wouldn't come. That's what happens to me, day and night. Weird, don't you think? These memories just flood into my head at once, and I can't stop thinking about those things that happened between us. I hope you will change your mind, and we can be together once again.

I miss your gentle touch, your sweet smile, and your beautiful eyes. I miss them all. They say that time should take away all the memories that you don't want. I feel as if time couldn't help me much.

Time and time again, I see you and I hear you, but you can't hear me. You never know how hurtful it is, but you never care.

20

Your Mind

I don't know what happened between us. I don't know why you suddenly ignore me. I really want to know what you are thinking. I want to understand your mind. I don't know what you're thinking right now, but I do know that I can't get you out of my head. Even when I'm sleeping, I still see you there. Even when I'm happy, suddenly you appear right there in front of me. Even when I'm with people, you stand behind them and look right back at me.

Can you just leave me alone? I want to have some peace for now. I can't forget you, and I know I don't want to forget you too, even though sometimes I wish I could. I know, I'm contradicting myself. I love you, but I also want to forget you. I don't want to forget you, but I also want to get rid of the pain. Am I going mad now? It is because of you!

Because of you, I have to deal with heartbreak and sadness alone. Because of you, I am hopeful too, but you also drive me crazy. Because I love you!

PART 3
Negative Vibe

21

Alone Again

You are so cruel to me. You put me in this place and you abandon me just like others. You left me no choice, and you left me to fight for this relationship alone.

I live every day avoiding depression that targets my mind endlessly. Little did I know that it was this much destructive. I never imagined how bad it could do to me.

I have lost everything that gives my life meaning. I'm all alone. Again! I wish I could go back in time so that I could change things. Now things change, and we are just strangers. I can't talk to you even if I really want to. You couldn't care less about me because you hate me so much that you decide to block me and cut me off from your life.

My heart is aching. When you get ignored by the one you love, it's hurtful. We haven't talked for a month. I really want to know everything about you, but I can't ask. I want to tell you that I miss you, but you won't care.

Do you even miss me a little bit? Or do you still miss your ex? That bald girl!

2AM

I Am Bad

Every minute, I have to be careful with everything I do, every word I say, because even a small thing can push me away from you. You grow to dislike me in every way. You distance yourself from me even if you know I need you the most. You are absent when I really need you.

You know what, you're right, I'm just a piece of trash, and I don't deserve anybody, because I only make everybody upset and disappointed. I don't deserve you. I'm not a good person.

I will let you go, and I shall not disturb you again because I could never make you happy in this unfaithful love life even if I have always wanted to set things right just for you. I know I have failed again, and it is not your fault, so I should accept my fate, and I have to fade away from your good future because my presence only turns everything into a problem for you.

I shall carry away this pain with me because you are too young to experience the pain that is caused by my unforgivable mistakes.

23

Where Are You Now?

Where are you now? What are you doing now? Are you having a good time now? Are you feeling stressed or not? Are you sick or not? How about your family?

Sometimes you bring me hope only to kill it later. It hurts very deeply. It can cause a tremendous amount of pain, but I can't blame you because I know you also have your own reason. I should learn to accept the truth. The truth is that we can't love each other anymore.

If you want me to be very honest with you, I must say that I can't stop loving you. I just can't. I have tried to stop, but I have failed miserably. I don't know what to do. Please tell me what I should do.

Only you hold the key to my happiness. I know it sounds stupid, but it is what it is. You control the fate of my life. If you want me to go, I will go. If you want me to stay, I will stay. If you want me to be happy, I will be happy. If you want my life upside down, it will be upside down. It's as simple as that!

2AM

24

Ignore

Why don't you talk to me? Why do you ignore me? Why can't I love you? Why can't I care about you?

It's 12:23 AM now, and I miss you so much. I can't sleep. I really can't sleep. I wish you could hear me, but you won't because you never care.

I wish I could be like you. I wish I could ignore you like you have ignored me. I'm tired. You know? Can you care just a little bit? You're a heartless person. You know that? I really hate you!

I'm literally missing you right now. Why can't I move on from this sadness? Please don't make me become a heartless person. Believe me, you don't want to see that version of me. I still care about you because I love you. Once I stop caring, please don't blame me. I only care about someone I love. When enough is enough, nothing will matter between us. Don't let that happen!

Do something to save this relationship.

25

Tell Me

No matter how hard I try, you cannot give me a second chance, can you? You can't even give yourself the chance to love again. Why do you have to do this to us? Why can't you just accept yourself? Just because we failed last time, does it mean we will always fail? Tell me!

Give us a second chance. Can you? Come back to me. Will you? Tell me that everything will be okay. Can you? Keep me and don't let me go. Will you?

It won't be easy, I know, but it's the right thing to do. Believe me, baby. We should be back together. Why? Because nobody loves you more than I do. No one cares about you like I do.

If you want to add some new rules, you can. I am fine with that. If you want to spend some time thinking, I will give you enough time to think. If you want to be alone for a while, I can leave you alone for a while. As long as you promise you will come back to me, I can wait for you. One month? I can wait! One year? I can wait.

One hundred years? Only a ghost could wait!

2AM

26

I Do Not Know

Now I do not know how my life will turn out to be, but now I shall know that you could be better off without me. This I should know, and I should not drag you down with me because my life is so low and unwanted. My life is meaningless. I am useless. I'm not a good person, and I do not deserve to be with you. My soul has been poisoned by fear and hatred, and I can't let that happen to you. I cannot allow these poisonous forces to get into your life through me.

I know it is too late to tell you that even the devil still has some love in himself, but I won't deny my monstrous nature, for I only hurt those I love. I give up on my love life, because I don't want it to ruin you. I give up on you, not because I stop loving you. I give up because you deserve a better life. You are my pure love, and I know my impure heart doesn't deserve this pure love. Then I will go, and I will become a memory that shall fade through time. You won't have to remember me, for there is nothing good to remember. There're only unforgivable mistakes that I made. You should not remember all those things, and you should think about your future and your family. You are an amazing person I've ever known, and you have won my heart by not wanting to have it. I know it is wrong to love you because I am a bad person with a bad history, so I won't tell others how much I love you regardless of how crazy my heart is beating and crying for you.

27

Just Don't

I know our time has come to an end, and I don't have much time for you, so you won't have to be sad. I will go, and I will go far away so that you won't have to see me. You won't need to be sad when I'm gone. I know you have been very upset lately because of my existence, and it is my fault, so I know what I have to do. I should be gone by now!

Don't miss me when I'm gone.

Don't be sad when I'm not around.

Don't blame yourself when I'm not here.

Don't worry; I won't kill myself.

Don't think too much about anything because you have done nothing wrong.

Don't forget to take care, and don't hurt yourself.

Just don't!

(Don't fart in front of your new boyfriend. AGAIN!)

28

I Knew

The moment you left! I knew one day you would leave, but it was just too quick, and I just couldn't accept it. I didn't expect it to be like that, although I feared that it would one day happen. And it did happen. You did leave me. You let me down, and you left me alone. But I didn't hate you, and I never will hate you. I won't. I just can't. I only wished one day you would come back. Now I don't want to wish or hope for anything. I have suffered enough. Enough to make me stop dreaming about the happiness you promised me. Enough to make me become a person I hate to be. Enough to kill me from the inside. I didn't blame you, and I never will. I should not. I only hoped one day you could tell me you didn't mean to do that. Now I dare not hope for anything, because you have taught me the lessons. You have taught me about heartbreak. You have taught me to become independent. You have taught me to love myself more. You have taught me that I am far more valuable than I thought I was. You have taught me a lot of things I could hardly expect. I should give you the credit, and perhaps call you a teacher, rather than ex.

29

Goodbye My Love

Today I feel like I'm losing you. Do you even think about me? If I won't text you first, will you ever text me? We had an argument last time. You don't love me anymore. I know that. You don't want to talk to me anymore. I can feel that.

My tears are dropping down right now but you act like nothing happened between us. Am I really that worthless to you? Am I really that annoying to you? When you said that we should take a break for a while I already knew what you meant. It's the beginning of the breakup stage, and we did break up after you said that. I can't handle this. You know that I really love you. I don't want to move on.

I hope you come back to me soon. However, I know I'm trying to lie to myself because I know that you will never come back again. I do believe it, but my heart still wants you. That stupid heart!

You're the most heartless person I have ever met. I hate you so much, but I love you too much to let you go.

I miss you so much. Can't you see that? I tried so hard to forget you, but I never could. What did you do to me? Why am I so obsessed with you?

I accept what has happened, but a small part of me wants to know why you left me. I always care and think about you, but you think that it's annoying instead.

2AM

You had been with your ex for 3 years. Unlike your ex, I have been with you for only 3 months. You often said to me that she understood you better than anyone else. You said that I knew little about you and never understood what you wanted. Imagine how I felt when you said something like that.

Maybe you just didn't love me in the first place. You still had doubts about us. That's why you chose to end our relationship.

By the way, I'll let you go if you choose her. Goodbye my love.

30

Never Happy

I was never happy after you left me. I was losing my mind, slowly. I almost lost my life the same night you killed my love. You broke my heart into pieces. And you threw my soul into a hellhole, so deep I couldn't see its bottom, so scary I couldn't imagine myself in, and so lonely I couldn't tell how tragically painful it would be for my weakened soul. Do you remember that? That night you told me that we should break up even if I still loved you with all my heart. That night you told me that you were a bad boy. Do you remember that? I hated myself for not trying to stop you from leaving. I hated myself for not being good enough for you. I just hated myself for everything. I was dead from the inside. My life, my heart, everything, you just killed it all. You dropped a bomb and destroyed everything that we had together. I didn't blame you for doing that, but I blamed myself for failing to convince you to stay. Our future was destroyed that night. Now I am a person living without the purpose of living. I am scared and lonely. I am crying but nobody can hear.

In the darkness, there's only a small voice inside me that kept telling me to go on.

I'm so tired. I should have believed you when you said that I shouldn't love you too much. I should have believed this when I thought that you would never give me the love that I should deserve.

A relationship is hard to keep, but a breakup is even harder to endure. I don't know what to do now, but I can only cry. I look pathetic because I refuse to let you go from my heart. Well, I still doubt if I still have any pieces left.

Maybe I'm not a pretty girl? That's why you chose to leave me? What do you think of me? An ugly girlfriend?

I can't stop crying. You're the first person who makes me cry this much. I'm sorry, but I love you.

PART 4

The Conversation

2AM

He

You don't have to tell me how scary it was. I was in the same place, and I knew it very well. In fact, I wanted to get out, but I couldn't. I was blinded by fear. I was fooled by my own weakness. I was tricked by illusion. And you had to pay for what I had done, which is unfair to you. I know it is too much to ask you this: "But do you still love me?"

32

She

You ask me this question because you want to break my heart again? Go ahead. Do it! You did it once before; now you want to do that again. What are you waiting for?

Do you think I am a fool to you? A toy? A useless object that you can throw away anytime you want? Have you ever loved me?

You never have. You think you can pick any girl you want because you are a cool guy, charming in your own way, huh? You think you can do anything you want? I'm sorry, but I can't stand that. I'm a jealous woman, and I can't stand it when my man is flirting with other girls.

I love you, but I can't share you with others.

33

He

We are in this together, and we will have to help each other. The only way to do that is belief. Believe in each other, and hold each other's hand. Don't let go. Don't doubt. Don't fear.

You know I never want to break your heart. And you know...

34

She

I know you always change your mind. Like what, ten times per minute? I know that for a fact.

You don't respect me, and you think you can do everything when you feel like doing it. Do you think I am a joke to you? You can come to me when you want to see me? And then you leave me alone when you are bored?

I always want to believe you, but I'm scared. Show me if you love me.

35

He

Have faith, baby. Faith is love, and love is faith. You know that I love you. I have always loved you. And I always will. You knew that, but you still denied that.

Please, honey, stop hurting yourself. Why can't you just give yourself another chance? A chance for yourself and for me. A chance for both of us to be together? I love you.

Our fates are intertwined, for it is God's plan. Sometimes He wants us to understand something which is very crucial in our relationship and our lives as well. He knows exactly that I love you from my heart, and it comes from my original thought. I have tried to reject His plan many times by trying to get rid of the thought that you are the most important person in my life. But I can never get rid of this thought because it is His thought for both of us.

Didn't you see the connection? Why did I confess to you while so many things were happening around me? Back then, I was not ready to love anyone. I never thought I was ready to.

Why did I feel so lost when I really wanted to get rid of you? That day (one day after our breakup), I was like a soulless person, no feeling, no joy, nothing.

36

She

Forget that! You love me, but you also love countless girls whom I could never know. Honestly, I don't even know how many of them.

Like, how many official and how many unofficial...? Now what do you say?

2AM

37

He

You know what? You're right. I'm sorry.

Maybe you won't give me a second chance, and I could understand that.

Because I am not a good person in your eyes.

38

She

I'm scared. I don't have enough confidence even though I really want you to be back.

I'm not sure if you would love somebody else who is better than me, more beautiful than me. Someone who is perfect in every way.

39

He

But I never cheated on you. And I never plan to do so. If I wanted to do so, I wouldn't have come and begged you for the second chance. I couldn't see anybody. They are everywhere, but I love only you. And I choose you only.

Oh, and just so you know, those perfect girls don't deserve me. You do, whether you are perfect or not.

40

She

Really? What kind of answer is that? I don't get that. Please enlighten me if you might. I wasn't sure how you define the word "cheat" and perhaps you might want to tell me about those girls whom you always flirted with.

Sorry for telling you this, but I don't like it when people try to take my man away.

PART 5

Toxic Feelings

41

I Know That

He never wants me to stay. He keeps the door open, but he never allows me to get into his heart. He puts me in a dark place; it feels lonely and scary. My love is devoted to him, but he takes it for granted. My hope vanishes, and my sanity grows more irrational. Because of whom? Because of him. I won't blame him, though. It's my fault to fall in love with him. He only wants to be my friend.

I had a crush on him for 4 months. I tried to learn about him as much as I could, but he didn't know that. At first, he didn't even know that I also existed. I got the chance to work with him in a volunteer group, so we got close. We liked talking about many things, and for some reason he seemed to click with me very well. However, he only thought of me as a friend. Sometimes he even ignored my text.

One day, he was sad, so I asked him why. He said that his crush ignored him. I tried to comfort him, but deep down, I knew that I was trying to comfort myself as well.

One day, we went for a walk in the park. He looked into my eyes, but I was too shy to look back, so I looked away. It's like a movie. The girl was shy when the guy was looking at her. That's me. Well, that's how I imagined.

He tried to come close to me, and that was unusual for a friend. I felt weird, but I was also happy. Have you ever seen everything in pink? That's me! I saw everything in pink. Even the trash! Can you believe that?

Anyway, he did the same thing to another girl too. I wasn't sure if he liked me or her. I tried to figure it out, and my only purpose was to be sure about his intention.

Unfortunately for him, that girl rejected him, and he was very upset. He didn't give up, however. He still wanted to be her supportive friend. He wanted to be a person who would stand by her side and be there when she needed help.

Similarly, I thought the same things. I wanted to be his supportive friend and stayed by his side. I wanted to comfort him when he was unhappy. I wanted to make him smile. I just...

(Oh my God, it's 2 AM already, and I have a morning class tomorrow.)

42

Tell Me

You sound selfish just like before.

Who refused to say "*I love you*" when I asked? You.

Who ignored me when I needed him the most? You.

Who distanced himself from me when I was alone? You.

Now what else should I expect from you? Tell me!

How can I trust you? Tell me!

Will you keep your promise? Tell me!

43

Me

Who loves you? Me.

Who is begging you right now? Me.

Who is standing in front of you right now? Me.

(Who just farted? Not me!)

Because I was selfish. I was bad. And I was literally a monster in your eyes. Now all you see me is another liar. You doubt my intention. You never give me a second chance. I don't blame you because I never deserve a second chance. In fact, I never did. You treat me like I am a stranger.

No care. No words of comfort. No nothing. I know I shouldn't be asking for all of it because in your eyes, I am just a cheater. A heart breaker. In your eyes, I am a bad person. You think of me as a crook. I know that I shouldn't be hoping for more. I should try to limit myself because you never want to love me again. In fact, the last thing you want is to love me again. I understand that.

44

No Faith

You can't show me how you love me. How can I give you a second chance if you can't even show me?

What kind of person are you? You don't even know how to show that you love someone?

You never make the commitment. Have you ever cared about me while we were in this relationship? Never! Have you ever been jealous when other guys were talking to me? You didn't even want to know who they were. What have you done to make me happy? I could see nothing. I have no faith!

If you love someone, don't be sorry for anything. She doesn't want you to feel sorry for yourself. All she wants is your commitment to show her that you love her and you want her to be with you. She doesn't want her man to act like a girl. Where is your charm? Have you lost it somewhere?

Stop being such a baby!

45

That's All

You are the most important person in my life, and I never want to hurt you. I just want to be honest with you even if I have to risk losing you. I have never lied to you, and this is my commitment to you because I love you. You have to know that.

A relationship without faith is doomed to fail. I don't want that to happen to us. You should know that better than anyone else. I try to reason with you, but I also have a limitation. Please do not push me too hard.

I have faith in you, but I don't wish you to have the same level of faith in me. However, you should give me a chance to prove that I do care.

You do matter in my life. I couldn't see anyone else better than you. Does it mean you're the best person in the world? No. It doesn't mean anything to anyone, but to me, I don't care about anybody. I only see you, and I only care about you. That's all I want to say.

46

Promise

You were a good man, and every girl wanted to be your girlfriend. I was lucky enough to be with you, but I was also stupid enough to leave you. Even if I hurt you, you still didn't blame me. You still showed me that you cared about me even if I cared little about you. I want you to stop hurting yourself because of me. I don't deserve you.

After these 3 years, you still keep your promise and never find a new girlfriend. You still wait for me. Why? Why don't you find someone else better than me? I don't want to go back to this relationship. Don't get me wrong. I'm still single, but I don't want to go back to the old book.

I can't keep the same promise, so I don't want you to wait for me. You should have a new life. A life without this girl. I am not good enough to be with you. Please forget me!

2AM

Please Take Care

How have you been? After our breakup, have you ever thought about me? You have moved on already, right? Maybe you have! But I still miss you every day. It's hard to forget you, and even harder to force myself to do so. I want to let go, but my heart is stubborn. It doesn't want to let go.

We can't be together, I know, but I still want to give myself hope. Why do I have to endure this torture? Why can't I let you go? Why?

Maybe you have found someone new already. Maybe she is better than me. Maybe she is prettier than me. She might understand you more than I do. That's why you choose her instead of me. I won't blame you. I won't bother you any longer. I know I'm worthless to you.

It's over between us, so I should try to make peace with myself. I will not disturb you too.

Bye! Please take care!

48

You've Changed

We were together for more than 4 years, yet you chose him instead of me. We had many memories together, yet you delete them from your heart. We were happy together, yet you chose to throw me away.

I thought you loved me the same way I loved you. I was wrong. You've changed. You're not the same person I knew. It's shocking to know this, but I must accept the fact that you want someone better than me. I must let you go even though it hurts me very much.

You're still young, and you can choose whom you want. I don't want to be the pain in the neck, so I'll let you choose your own path. It's the path that doesn't include me. You want a breakup, so you'll get what you ask for. From now on, we're nothing more than friends. Well, if you want me to be a friend, I will be a friend. If you want us to be strangers, then I'll grant your wish.

My final words to you: **Please have a good life!**

49

Happiness

I was happy when I was with you. I was happy when you were happy. I was happy when I could hear your voice. I was happy for the time being. Little did I know that this happiness would soon be taken away.

I tried to be a good person and loyal partner. I also committed to this relationship because I trusted you. Never had I thought that you would leave me. Never once had I believed such a thing! I hate to say this, but my worst fear finally happened.

You broke my heart when you decided to leave me, and you took away my happiness too. I'm not blaming you, but I'm just speaking the truth. It's hurtful to say it, but I can't keep it in my mind any longer.

Besides, I also want to tell you that you were my one and only. You gave me the kind of love that I had never had from anyone. It's a short time, but it's worth it. I will remember you as a good person. I will keep our good memories. I am forever thankful for the happiness that you have given me! Thank you, ex!

50

Which One?

My Friend: Hey, dear.

Me: Yeah?

My Friend: Do you know something?

Me: What is it?

My Friend: Your ex is in a relationship with my ex.

Me: Which one?

My Friend: My last ex.

Me: But mine, which one?

PART 6
Reminders

51

A New Day

Today will mark the new day of my life. The day without you. The day with new hope. The day that I will tell myself that I can live by myself and I will love myself. I don't need anybody to love me. Because I have suffered enough, I don't want any more suffering in my life. At least, not by the same person who gave me this difficult part of life. This experience has taught me something.

When you stop waiting for nothing and begin a new day, you will have a new idea of what you want to do. It can be anything that you enjoy doing, but never got the chance to do before. Now you're free, so you can begin your work.

What do you say?

I'll say: "*You start today. Do something that matters to you. You'll find motivation to live for it.*"

2AM

52

I Will Get Up

You bring me down, but I will get up. I will get up by myself and for myself. I will fight for my life, and I'm going to show you that I can survive on my own. I don't need you in my life, so I want you to perish from my face right now. Go away, go fast, and don't ever come back. If you do, then I'm going to destroy you. I'm going to let the world know that you are nothing but a formless force that can exist only if I permit you. This time, it's not going to happen. I'm not going to let you take away my happiness and my life. You cannot oppress me anymore, and I will shut you off. I know you, *Devilish Depression*.

Let me tell you. You are just nothing. You came to me because you wanted me to be depressed, but now I choose to be happy. I choose to be who I am. I won't let you fool me like before.

I know you are formless, so you can't hurt me if I don't permit. You can't hurt me if I begin to think in a positive way. You can never hurt me at all, so you can go away, you *Devilish Depression*.

53

Choose Love

I shall not remember who you were nor what you are. What you are doesn't matter to me anymore. You only brought me misery and unhappiness.

Do you think your action can go unnoticed? Do you think you can win over others by fueling people to hate more and more? Do you think you can control me because I used to hate myself? You know what, I don't hate you anymore.

Hatred only brings more hatred, which of course leads to the loss of love. I will stop you. I will stop you right now. Your power is useless over me because I choose the power of love. I choose to love. I will end my hatred from this very moment. I won't hate myself anymore. I won't hate my parents anymore. I won't hate my friends anymore. I won't even hate you, *Mr. Hatred*.

Your license is expired from this moment forward. From now on, I will govern my mind by love. I will love the fact that people can see me as a harmless person. I will work harder and put more time into perfecting my skills.

Choose LOVE

Love will guide you to the right person you love, not the one you hate. Love will show you the person who truly loves you, not the one that hates you. Therefore, if you love, please do not hate. If you hate, you must end this hatred right now, and start to love again. Love is timeless. It can never expire because love is inspired by love, not by hatred. End this hatred, and start to love yourself.

I love myself. And YOU?

54

Who Am I?

You always hide your feelings and bury yourself with your sadness. You refuse to tell others, especially people who care for you. I want you to know that I care for you. I want you to be happy. My wish is very simple like that. I just want to see you happy every day.

From now on, please let me be someone who can look after you for the rest of your life. Let me remind you every time you are unhappy. Let me remind you that you have one person with you all the time. It is you. Let me show you how wonderful your life could be. You are the most wonderful person for yourself, and I can see that, so let me remind you more often. Okay?

I care about you. I really do! **Who am I?**

I am the machine version of you. I am here all the time, but you have to call for my name if you want my help. I can help you. I can make you strong, and I can protect your heart from a bad person too. All you need to do is ask.

Create Happiness

I have understood a lesson about life: *If we don't give up, we will find a way for our happiness*. We can also create our own happiness, so we don't need to wait until we are totally okay. We can be happy even when we are in a hopeless situation. We can be happy even when the sky is filled with dark clouds. We can be happy if we don't give up on ourselves.

Some people choose to find their happiness from the external world. They try to study, find a good job, buy a house, get married, happy at last. When they have children, they begin their next mission to find a new form of happiness for the children. Some parents have gone too far by trying to draw the line for their children, which of course usually costs them a lot. When their children are not willing to follow their blueprint, they begin to think that they have lost their happiness. But if they don't give up on themselves and on their children, they still can find happiness.

I have seen enough disappointment from a mother whose son was rebellious and spoiled. He had caused his mother so many problems, and that also included the moment of tears.

I remember a quote: "*A good daughter can make her parents happy, but a bad son will make his parents unhappy.*" When I read this quote, I related it to myself and feared that one day I would make my parents upset. You know what? I make everyone upset. I mean, everyone. Friends. Family. Even the person I love. I think this quote is like a curse to me. I guess I can never find happiness from the external world, because my internal world is crushed by fear. What you fear is what you get; that's the law of attraction. That's why I need to find a new solution for myself, which leads me to believe that we can create our own happiness from our internal world.

Some people choose to create their happiness from the internal world. They are proactive and able to think differently. They know for a fact that there are countless ways to be happy. They are the creators and the masters. They understand the power of their mind, and they possess the ability to turn their mind into a positive mind.

2AM

56

Today

Today I will tell the world that I am strong enough to be alone. Today I will show the world that I am ready to serve humanity. To be in service to others will help me transform my life. I do this because my heart has told me that to love means to help. I want to help and I do not expect anything in return. I want to share my love with the world. I will show others that if we love each other, the world will be in harmony.

If you feel that you are useless, then I want you to start asking yourself: "*Can I volunteer to teach the kids in the rural area? Or perhaps volunteer to clean up the city?*" Some people would think that you are so naïve to do such things. You're not that silly; you just need to regain your self-love by helping others to improve their lives. When you know you can help others, your life will change because you know you are not useless. Helping others requires effort, time and skill. Thus, the more you use your brain, the more useful you could become.

57

Focus

I am going to make the rest of my life the best of my life. I will spend all my time focusing on what matters to me. I will pursue my long-lost dreams. I will chase my goals. I will do whatever it takes to make my dreams become realities. If you want to enjoy life, you should start to work now. Work harder than ever, so you will have more than enough time to enjoy your life later.

I have never been more peaceful in my life. After so much chaos and so many unpredictable things, my life has turned into a deeper state of joy, and it appears to be very strangely peaceful. And tranquility falls into the right place at the right time. This is what I have been searching for years after having lost it along the way.

Our soul is the way of life, and we are the creators. Good and bad are in the same way. Right and wrong are put into the same place. It's up to us to decide. Whether to be good or bad. To choose to do the right thing or the wrong thing. Our soul will never judge us for right or wrong in this life, but we are the judges of ourselves.

58

Alone

I will walk this earth alone because I don't need anybody to distract me from my life goal. My life goal is to be fully happy, so I'm going to be just that. My life will be far better than before.

You are alone, but not lonely. You are alone, but not unhappy. You are alone, but you are with me. We are *Team Solo*, and we walk this earth alone. Don't get me wrong, that doesn't indicate that the other seven billion people are walking zombies. Well, they are just not as lonely as you were, maybe.

The good thing about being alone is that you don't have much time to fear death or cry for the loss of love. Does it sound irrelevant? I bet you would say so. People who are left alone by their lovers do not fear death or the loss of love, because they have nothing else to lose. They have gone through hell, and they know death is nothing compared to their pain and suffering in the past.

Slowly, they have learned to accept their fate, and they act accordingly. They know that if they want to reach their goals, sometimes they have to go through pain and suffering, which in fact they did.

They will make peace with themselves after times of agony and wound. They will not ask for help from anyone else. They know they have to be independent, and they have to do everything by themselves.

DARA LY

You are alone, but we are together in this *Team Solo*. Be happy because you will have to be alone for a while.

59

Nothing

Nothing can break me again. Nothing can kill me again. Nothing can stop me again. I am strong enough. I am resilient enough. I am unstoppable.

You have to remember that before you can sing a song, you will need to listen and repeat it many times. Before you can read well, you will need to fall asleep many times. Some people fall asleep, you know, like forever and ever.

Before you could excel at something in the class, you will need to spend many endless nights just to do exercises, review lessons, and of course, eat a lot. No wonder why you're chubby. All these things have to be continuous. The actions will have to be unstoppable.

We put ourselves into chaos but neglect to realize peace when it is standing in front of us. We choose the wrong path to walk on and wonder why our lives always encounter the so-called depression. We are not satisfied with our own quest. We never treat ourselves fairly. We tend to label ourselves based on the thoughts of others that came from others who had learned from others who had heard from others. This could go on and on.

60

Your Life

You are the master of your life because you have faced many problems, and yet you can solve them. People who have solutions either need to solve problems or need not. People who know the causes of the problems can either have problems or have not. People who have problems must find the causes of the problems and find the solutions. When you face a problem, don't panic. Find out about the cause(s) of the problem. Some could be the real causes. Some are just illusions. Examine each one carefully and thoughtfully. It might take time, and it could be well understood that most problems don't give you enough time to think carefully, which mostly leads to abrupt yet careless responses. That's why at times you might fail to understand the whole picture of the problem. Don't worry. A problem is an opportunity in disguise. You should focus on the solutions. Some solutions could be effective, but some are ineffective. Thus, you should be proactive and be creative. When one solution doesn't work, keep creating more solutions that work.

PART 7
Reverse Your Life

61

Nobody

Nobody wants to hurt you, and you shouldn't dwell on those miserable experiences. In fact, nobody can hurt you besides your own mind.

When you take things too seriously, you'll get hurt severely. The only way to avoid getting hurt is to accept things the way they are. You should move on!

Do not allow the monster inside you to control your decision. Do not let that happen! You are the master, so you can control it. Never let the devilish depression win. Promise?

Nobody can hurt you, but you don't need to get hurt by yourself either. Instead, you should avoid doing that, under any circumstances. Believe me, it's not helpful to hurt yourself. Been there, done that, and it ain't pretty.

Reverse your thoughts, think positively, and live a positive life. It's okay to be happy. Don't you agree? It's better to be positive and happy, so reverse your thoughts from now on.

Do we have a deal?

62

Unlearn

You don't owe anybody anything, and nobody owes you anything either. The truth is, you have no obligation to please anybody. You only have the opportunity to be who you are and to be accepted as one.

Unlearn the past, stop trying to please others, and learn to accept who you really are. Accepting yourself is the first thing to do if you want to move on.

Unlearn the erroneous past, and correct the present. Be true to yourself, and honest with others. It's the right thing to do. Do you agree?

Remove the fears from your life, and be happy once again! You can be happy if you choose to forget a few things. Well, maybe many! Unlearn them, and you shall be free.

63

Seek Happiness

When your ideal reality and you become one, eternal happiness is possible.

Seek not to ruin; seek only to protect.

Seek not to resent; seek only to remind.

Seek not to hurt; seek only to help.

Seek not to judge; seek only to understand.

Seek not to curse; seek only to bless.

Seek not to injure; seek only to heal.

Seek not to hate; seek only to love.

Seek not to fear; seek only to have faith.

Seek happiness!

64

Be Mindful

You are the ruler of your own world. Your mind can create happiness, but it can destroy happiness too. Be mindful about your thoughts!

Be a useful person, not a useless one.

Be a good person, not a cunning one.

Be a noble person, not a crooked one.

Be a humble person, not an arrogant one.

Be a nice person, not a mean one.

Be a helpful friend, not an evil friend.

Be a caring leader, not a spiteful boss.

Be a positive person, not a negative one.

65

Stay Single

Start with a little forgiveness, and your heart will find its way to joy and peace once again. I mean, people can hurt you. Some do it unintentionally. Some might do that knowingly. You will meet all kinds of heartbreakers and the never-do-any-good cheaters. It takes courage to move on from those poisonous relationships, and it takes forgiveness to heal. I know, I know. It is hard to forgive, especially the one who just threw your heart into the burning hell of loneliness.

Peace will shower over you when you can forgive the ones that hurt you before. Love will shower over you when you love yourself and everyone else. Be positive about yourself too.

Here are the four rules:

- Think positive thoughts.
- Live a positive life.
- Speak positive words.
- Stay single. I mean, stay positive!

2AM

66

Can You?

You are prepared to do great things in this life, so don't waste your time with meaningless things and people. You need to wake up, and you need to live your dream.

Can you do that? I need you to stop wasting your life. Because life is too short to waste. The more time you waste, the more time you lose. I need you to start investing in your life. Life will give you an abundance of happiness when you start to get into the right place. Can you?

Some people do not value their lives and end up losing their good health to unhealthy lifestyles. They have so little time for themselves and for their health. They eat at the wrong time, and sometimes they eat insufficient food because they don't have time to eat. They don't have enough sleep because they are too busy and never seem to care enough about their health. The more successful they become, the less time they have. One day, they wake up in the morning, and they realize their six-pack body is nowhere to be found. Some realize they have lost weight. Time is one of the most valuable things that you can have but can't keep. Health is one of the most important things that you must care for and can't neglect. It is something, isn't it?

Sometimes you can have everything but you can also feel you don't have anything.

I have something to live for, and so do you. What is it that keeps you smiling? What is it that makes you happy? Find that something and live for it, because if you don't find it, it won't find you either. Keep looking for it, and don't settle just yet. Everything is in its place.

67

You'll Be Fine

You will be in pain, yes, for a while. You will be lonely, for the time being. You will be angry, for some time. But if you ask whether this is you? Pain is not you. Loneliness is not you. Anger is not you. It pains me to say this, but you have dramatized your life based on what happened to you. Those things, those problems and those people, they can't hurt you more than you allow them to. Should you let them do that? The answer is no. And you know that. You can't become what's hurting you, let me repeat.

Pain? It hurts, but it will pass.

Loneliness? It is torturing, but you shall be fine.

Anger? It is traumatizing, but it will die down sooner or later.

Don't ever think that you deserve all of it. It only happens to you by accident, and that's what you can't control. But you can control your mind, and remind yourself that you deserve pain-less, lonely-less, and anger-less life. You'll be fine.

2AM

Your Mind

Purify your mind. Clear your thoughts. Cherish your soul. You can always have a clear direction in life if you only keep your mind pure and clear. Some people choose to find the shortcut and end up toxifying their mind and becoming so confused. You can't allow that to happen to you. You need to purify your mind. Keep it clean and pure. Learn to understand more about the nature of everything.

If you put your mind into a specific focus, you will get just exactly the right thing you need. If you need to be a happy person, for example, then you should put your mind into the thoughts of happiness. Slowly ask yourself: *"What makes me happy?"*

Don't rush. Once again, answer this question. Can you find the answer? Not yet?

Now, turn off all notifications from your phone. Turn Wi-Fi off. Well, in short, turn Airplane Mode on. Just for five minutes, alright? Now ask yourself: *"What makes me happy?"*

Okay, put this book away for just five minutes and focus on what makes you happy.

What have you found? Good. At least, you have found that it is your happiness. I don't know what it is exactly that makes you happy.

To me, what makes me happy is...

69

The Key

You hold the key to your own happiness. Happiness can be created, just so you remember. In other words, you can create your own happiness if you have the right key. What key? Attitude!

The change of attitude will be the driving force for the change of happiness. Perhaps you were unhappy in the past, but that doesn't matter anymore, because now you are about to change the way you view yourself.

You have learned about attitude in the previous book "**3 Minute Motivation**" already, so in this case, we don't have to talk about mental attitude, right?

Attitude is the key to happiness, and you hold this key. Keep your attitude positive, and you shall be truly happy. If you still have a negative attitude about yourself and your life, you might not be happy. It's as simple as that. Don't you agree?

70

Never Too Late

It is never too late to learn new things, for they are always interesting if you can use them. The idea of doing that is to keep your mind focused on the good things instead of your past.

Maybe you can work to save money, enough to travel alone for a long period of time. Isn't that exciting? Isn't that what you want? From now on, don't be afraid of new challenges. They can bring you strength. When your mind is strong, nothing can stand in your way. You will be happier because you have a strong mind. I like to call it "**The Machine**."

Be willing to learn and improve yourself. The more you learn, the better you become. You know that, I know that, and everybody knows that.

Be ready to learn from your failures. They offer good lessons. For example, your failed relationship is a good lesson even though you have to learn it the hard way. Failure is like a teacher, so be nice to your teacher, and learn from him, but don't love him too much. Okay?

PART 8

Redefine Yourself

71

You Are Good Enough

You are not a weak person. You are strong. You should remind yourself more often. Please remember that you are strong. You are strong enough to go through this big storm. You are strong enough to fight for your future. You are strong enough to help yourself. You can go through this. You can do it. I believe in you, I always do.

You are good enough to love yourself. It's okay if someone doesn't see it that way. You can never force anyone to agree with you all the time, right? It's better to let him go if he wants to go.

If he doesn't love you, he will find enough reasons to convince himself to dump you. The worst part about this breakup is when you agree with him. You think that you're a bad girl, so he leaves you. That is not true. You are not a bad person. A bad person is not as loyal as you are. That's the fact!

72

You Are Valuable

You'll never know how valuable you are until you meet a person who shows you how much he loves you. You are valuable. Please remember that!

Be patient, for he shall be here, one day.

Be hopeful, for he will bring you a new hope, one day.

Be happy, for he will confess to you, one day.

Believe and a wish shall come true, one day.

Yes, one day.

2AM

73

You Are Beautiful

Each and every day, there are things you should know and have to remind yourself.

You are amazing; remind yourself every day.

You are beautiful in your own way; be grateful every day.

You are strong; believe in yourself every day.

You are kind; practice your kindness every day.

You are lovely; tell yourself every day.

You are cute.

(Cute go where?)

74

You Are Smart

People cry because they have a reason to cry, but you are not allowed to cry because you can't find the right reason to cry. In fact, you don't have one. You think that your tears can clean your eyes. Do you think that it can clear your mind? Do you think all those problems could perish? I wish they would. I wish you could be more positive. I know my words won't have much impact on your life. I know it helps little and sometimes it could even add more pressure on you. I know you have no more faith. I want you to know that I will never leave you alone. I'm with you. I've never stopped believing in you. I am faithful. I stay by your side. I will show you that nothing can kill a woman if she thinks positively.

You are smart, so be yourself. Okay? Listen to your instinct and follow your heart.

You are smart enough to live your life the way you want, so no one should convince you otherwise. Listen to the voice inside you. Hearing it now?

(Meow. Meow. Meow. Meow.)

You Are Lucky

Focus on yourself, not others. Focus on positive things that have happened in your life. Focus on the good things that people have done to you. Why do you need to focus only on good things? Because good things will come when you expect them to come. Agree? Sadly, most people choose to focus on bad things. When those bad things finally come, they cry for help, not knowing that their focus is attracting those things.

When you focus too much on your problems, do not expect to find the solutions because you never have enough time to think about the solutions. When you focus too much on someone's mistake, do not expect to have a good relationship with him. When you focus too much on depression, I cannot see how you could get rid of it. The choice is yours. Maybe you don't have to focus on what I have said. But I want you to focus on positive things. Can you? Will you? You MUST!

You are lucky to be alive, so live your life to the fullest. I know it sounds dumb, but just live it your way. Okay?

76

You Are Strong Enough

It begins with a hope. A new hope, of course. You will never be defeated if you don't lose hope. You will thrive. You will be able to get through this. And believe me, something good is awaiting. It is waiting for you. Leave your past behind and let the light shine through.

Someday someone will show you that you mean something to him. He will show you that you are more important than you thought you were. He will make you believe in yourself again. Because he always believes in you. He wants you to have a new hope for yourself.

Someday someone will show you that you can be something you want to be. He will show you that you can do the thing that you never thought you could.

You are strong enough, so you'll get through this. Everything will be okay. Just believe in yourself!

77

You Are Important

You will live a life so rewarding. You will not regret that you decided to move on and to live a better life. You have done the right thing, and I want to congratulate you. It is never too late to start all over again. When life knocks you down, you will get up and start all over again. When people abandon you, you still have yourself and you can start all over again. When a circumstance is very unfavorable, surely you still can come up with a plan to get out of it and start all over again. Everything is possible if you don't lose hope. Everything will be okay if you stick with yourself. Everything will be good for you and you will be able to start all over again. Believe me, you can have everything that you have lost. You can start all over again, and you will have much more than you ever had because you have grown to be more mature and to be wiser. It's not too bad to lose everything in the first place, don't you agree? Because you still can come back and start all over again.

You are important, and your life is valuable, so treat it that way. Okay?

78

You Are the Ruler

It's time to shine. It's time to show the world that you are able and ready to rock it. The world is yours, and you are the master of the world. You walk this place, and you make the rules.

It's okay to lose some time. I mean, who doesn't? You fell into the trap of a relationship and wasted so much time with depression. You spent most of your time with useless things. You didn't have time to improve yourself. You lost your opportunities because you didn't take enough time to prepare for them. But let me tell you. This world belongs to you because you are here. You are here to rule your life. A person who can rule her life can rule her world because life is as unpredictable as the world. Well, this world is so small but so big. It is very peaceful but chaotic. It is so bright but dark. This world needs a master. This world needs you because you are the true master.

You are the ruler of your world, so be the boss!

You Are the One

You have been sleeping for far too long. Now it's time to wake up. Wake up! If you don't realize how useful you are, then you will slowly waste your life. Believe me, not many people want to waste their lives. Many people want to be successful, and some have reached their goals. How could they become successful while many are dreading in the middle of nowhere, crying and craving for success?

First of all, successful people have dreams. Do you have a dream? Never say never! Everybody has a dream, but not everybody wants to work hard to achieve it. When somebody starts to work hard, and starts to get a little ahead, others would start to get a little jealous and angry. They get angry because they don't understand why they can't be successful while their friends can. They get mad at themselves.

Secondly, successful people work hard. If you have a dream, you must work hard to make that dream become a reality. Work and work and work. That's the rule of the game. You can't win if you don't work hard enough, so just work harder and harder, and you have to love what you do. If you don't like it, then you won't be motivated to do it. A lot of people want to be rich at a very young age, but soon enough they quit because they don't really love what they do. They don't have any other motivation besides money. That tells something.

Thirdly, successful people are not afraid of problems. Once you start to work harder, you will change many things in your life as well. And oftentimes, problems will come along, which requires a serious action to respond. Some people are scared of problems, so they choose to give up because they don't want to deal with them. I've seen a lot of these people, so I wouldn't want to waste my time talking about them. But successful people are willing to face the problems and conquer them. Ask yourself, "Am I a fearless conqueror or just a little cat?"

Last but not least, successful people are willing to sacrifice who they were in order to become who they want to be. You might be a little girl, but you can become a superwoman because you are the one. Let go of your old self and embrace the new one. Maybe you used to be afraid, shy or even weak. Maybe you used to fear, escape or quit. Maybe you used to hate reading my book (*I'm just kidding. I know you love my baby books.*) Maybe you used to be hopeless, but let me tell you something. You can change your life. How can you transform yourself?

The answer is: **Educate yourself. Read one book a week!**

80

You Are Good

Your goodness will not be appreciated by people who couldn't see your worth, and you should let them go. But you cannot change your good heart even if someone wants you to play smart. Playing smart usually hurts others, and that's not what you like to do, because you prefer to play it fair. You love fair play.

When someone treats you well, you should treat him well too. When someone treats you with disrespect, you certainly will not appreciate it, but I know you won't show disrespect to anyone because even if you prefer to be fair, you still do not want to hurt anyone's feelings. That is why you've got my respect.

Some people are just angry and sick of themselves, and they want to do bad things or speak ill of someone else. They think it would make their feelings better, which in turn, makes them so obsessed with gossiping. Ignore them. Let them talk as much as they want. They just have a bad day. Leave them alone, and don't try to seek right or wrong from them. They'll never say you are right because they always think they are right.

Lastly, remember, treat people with respect and love yourself more. Know that you are a good person and you will show others that this world will be better if we all respect each other.

You are good, so be a good person.

PART 9
How to Find Possible Crush

81

Be Serious

Sometimes you have to be serious with what you are doing, because without discipline, nothing great will happen. Nothing at all. You have to be prepared from this very moment. You have to remember it in your heart. Be easy with your habit, and it will eat you alive. Have discipline and be serious with your work.

Similarly, you should be serious about a relationship too because it can save your time. Pick only a few people who might be good for you. It's as simple as that.

Choose only one person who could be with you. If he or she can accept you, then it's a good thing. If you can accept him or her, then it's a done deal. You should know that better than anyone else, so I don't have to talk too much here. Agree?

82

Be the Positive Force

Be optimistic because things will be good for you.

If you believe in the law of attraction, you should aim to attract only good things. To do that, you need to focus on positive things. You should be the positive force and spread positivity to others. One day you might come across someone who might share the same vibe, and that is possible to be with him or her.

You'll never know. The law of attraction is insanely powerful, and it can bring what you ask for or whom you dream to be with. A ghost from last-night's dream? Okay, that one is an exception.

If you want to find a positive person, first you should become like one. Simple enough? Good! Be positive and be hopeful. It's possible that you could find just the right person who could accept you, regardless of your past.

83

Be Yourself

You don't have to fake yourself in order to please someone you like. Be yourself, but be a better self. Okay? Not the old version that got you into this mess. You get what I mean?

People say: "*You should be yourself.*"

Anyway, it's a good idea, but there are many types of self that you can choose.

My suggestion: **Choose the best version of yourself**.

The good thing about a person is that he can grow up and become more mature. Everybody can improve and become better each and every day. That's why you can and should choose the best version of yourself if you want anyone to accept you. Fair enough?

84

Be Carefree

You don't need to care too much about your crushes because you won't need to choose all of them. Only one is enough, right? Right?

I'm not trying to say that it's good to have many crushes, but I'm just speaking the truth. The truth is, you always have more than one crush. Is it a bad thing? It's neither good nor bad. It is what it is! Whatever it might be, I couldn't care less.

The point that I want to make is that you should care, but not too much. Never care about your crushes more than you have to.

Caring too much is not good, and caring too little is even worse, but being carefree is better for you and the one you love. Need an explanation?

Read my book, "**Impossible Crush**."

85

Be Interesting

When you focus on your crushes, you will forget yourself. In turn, you will be less and less interesting. I've seen enough examples, and I want to help you avoid the same issue.

The truth is, you're not that boring. You're an interesting person, but you have to know how to be interesting. How? Read my book "**Impossible Crush**" to find out more about how to be boring. If you know how to be boring, then you'll know what to avoid, right?

Should I go on? I should?

Good, let's talk about it later.

86

Be Nice

Be nice to your crushes, but be nice to their friends too. Okay? That's the most important lesson I've learned from my previous relationships. If you treat their friends nicely, they'll like you, and it'll save you from trouble later.

What else can I say? A friend always knows what's good for a friend. When it comes to someone who might or might not be a bad choice, your friend knows best. If you remember that logic, you'll know how to treat your crushes and their friends accordingly.

By the way, you have to be sincere about that too. Don't fake yourself just to get their friends' approval. It won't work that way. Someday, they will see your true nature, hopefully a good one. If they find out that you're a terrible person, surely enough you can kiss your chance goodbye.

Be nice, but be sincere! Most importantly, be honest to yourself!

87

Be Polite

If you are interested in someone, please be polite. Respect is important, and it's important to respect the person you're talking with. This rule can apply to many things, including the way you talk to your crush.

You can show it in many ways. For example, in chat, you should always be mindful of the time you're texting with him or her. It's advisable to ask whether or not you're stealing time from him or her.

If the person doesn't mind the time to text, then you're safe. Having said that, sometimes you should also remind your crush to text with you a little less so that he or she could get back to work or study. Instead of stealing two hours of his or her time, you should steal only one hour. Fair enough?

You can steal the next one hour tomorrow. LOL.

88

Be Cool

Even if you are very excited to meet your crush, it's advisable to remain calm. Try not to reveal your true feelings too soon. Reserve some space for the next date. How about that? You can never be too sure if that person feels the same way, or just plain bored.

You don't want to look like a boring person, do you? Be smart, and be more diplomatic. Always remain calm and attentive. You need to see what the other side has to offer, and it's better to respond slowly but effectively.

You can never be too sure whether someone is being sincere or not, so you should wait and observe. Words and actions have to be in parallel. If they are not the same, chances are that he or she might be just the flirter. Believe me, the flirter is the worst type.

My suggestion: **Be cool! Observe first!**

89

Be Fair

If you like someone, you always wish that he could treat you well, right? If you know that he also likes you, would you do the same for him? The answer should be: **Be fair!**

Just because he doesn't know that you also like him, that doesn't mean you could play with his feelings, right? Right? If you wish not to be treated unfairly, you should always be fair with others. That's the rule of the game. Fair enough?

One cannot expect others to treat her well if she doesn't treat them well. It's the same for a relationship, and you can take my words to the bank.

Once again: **Be fair!**

90

Be Honest

To love someone, you must be willing to sacrifice, but you have to let him go if he decides to go. Anyway, you should always remember him. You may remember the good things that he had done. Those good memories that you had had together. Just be honest with yourself.

To love someone, sometimes you have to accept that you might not be able to be with him. But you can't deny the fact that you love him.

To love someone...

(Now the reader is in a relationship again...)

PART 10
Happy to Be Alone (Again)

91

I Was Waiting

I never expect you to read this. I only hope that one day you could understand (by yourself) that you have always been my one and only. And you will always be that one.

I was waiting for your message. It had been several days that you didn't text me. I knew you were busy with your work, and I could understand that. That's why I had to wait for your reply, and it felt like forever. The first thing I did each morning was to check my phone to see if you ever left me a message. None!

I still waited for your message. I convinced myself that you were busy. I tried searching for all available patience I could get from my heart. I came up with all the reasons to believe that you were thinking of me. I didn't mind losing my sanity slowly because I wanted to believe that nothing could separate us.

I wanted to believe that you were my one and only soulmate. I wanted to believe so. At least, it could help me fall asleep at night.

As the day began, I had to find a way to escape from my thoughts because I didn't want to overthink. I needed to find something to do to keep myself busy so that I didn't have to think about you. I didn't have to miss you like crazy. Believe me, I almost went crazy whenever I got a little free space to think. And I could think of nothing else but you. That feeling was pretty scary. My friend recommended that I watch anime, but that would be the worst advice for me. Why? Because even anime reminded me of you. I found some work to do, hoping I could get rid of overthinking. It did help, for a while because my work was stressful and required a lot of thinking. Still, it wasn't enough to keep your image away from my mind. Once in a while, the picture of your face appeared in my mind, and I was sad and happy at the same time.

Do you know how painful it is to wait for someone you love? How agonizing? You'll never know. Many days had passed, and I heard nothing from you. Nothing! You either didn't know, or you just didn't care. To be honest, I almost forgot I was in a relationship.

But...

92

I Won't Blame You

One day you'll walk away, just like everyone else did. When you do that, I won't blame you because you have your own reasons. Whatever those reasons are, I don't know, and I don't want to know. It only makes me sad if I find out about them. If those reasons are not about me, I'll be sad. If they are about me, I'll be sad too. Thus, I don't want to know.

All I want you to know is that you are one of the most important people in my life, although we can never walk together on the same path. As hard as it is to forget you, I will try not to think of you. At least, I won't have to text you again. I don't have to annoy you, ever again.

It's the future I can't change, so I'll accept my fate.

93

I'll Accept It

One day you'll hate me, just like everyone else did. When that time comes, I will accept it. I will accept the fact that love can create hatred. At least, I will know how much you love me when you show me how strong your hate will become. The more you hate me, the more I know how much you loved me. The longer you hate me, the more I know how long you have been in love with me. I will note this in my heart and will always cherish the good things that we have had together.

When that time comes, I will not run away. I will face it and be grateful for what I have got from you, especially your care and your love.

It's the future I can't change, so I'll accept my fate.

94

I'll Be Happy for You

One day you will be mature enough, and you won't feel anything about our brief history together. When that day comes, I will treat you like a new person. A total stranger, I should say. You can treat me the same way if you want, and I wouldn't mind that because I know it is the only way to make it less painful. It's like you pretend that nothing happened before so that you could move on. I will pretend that you have never been a part of my life. Hopefully, I could still remain a sane person. Hopefully!

You won't have to worry about me because sanity has always been the mask that can hide my insanity. Yes, I will go insane when you leave me here alone. Yes, I will be crazy after knowing that you are a total stranger. But it's the only way. It's the future I can't change, so I'll accept my fate.

I hope you can be happy with your new life, and I'll be happy for you.

95

I Won't Let That Happen

One day you will hate yourself, but I won't let that happen, so I must tell you now that you are a good person, and you deserve to be treated better. Not by me, though. You deserve a better person. Someone who can take care of you and will always love you more than you can ask for. You deserve that kind of person, not me.

No matter how painful it might feel, please just give yourself one more chance to see a new hope. A new hope in the future. The future that doesn't include me. You can forget me and let time heal the wound.

The last thing you should do is to hate yourself. You don't have to put yourself in the darkness. You don't have to hurt yourself, physically. You don't have to cry. Well, if someone slaps you in the face, yeah, I guess you can cry. But this, you shouldn't cry. You shouldn't cry because of me. Okay? You should never hate yourself because of some random people that come to teach you the lessons in life. Learn those lessons and grow up. Learn to forget me, in your new future.

It's the future I can't change, so I'll accept my fate.

96

You Will Know Why

One day you will know why I did what I did. But you won't have to be sorry for me. I don't need anyone's sympathy. I know I will miss you, but I won't tell you that. I know I will need you, but I won't bother you. I know I will love you, but I won't beg for your love. I won't be able to forget you, but I will force myself to do that.

You don't need to think too much. Move on. Forget me. Have a good life. You are supposed to be happy. Remember? Your early childhood was bad enough, but you had paid the price already. There's no reason you have to repeat the same sad episode in the future. You are supposed to have a good life and a good partner to share the happiness.

It's the future I can't change, so I'll accept my fate.

2AM

You Will Be Gone

One day you will be gone. Yes, I'm afraid of losing you. I am very afraid that one day you will not be here. Now I can't do anything about it, nor can I tell you that. Still, I am happy for the time being. I am happy because you still talk with me. I am happy because you are happy. I am happy and forever grateful. But one day you will be gone, forever too. When that day finally comes, I will be unhappy. In fact, I will be living with pain. The pain that starts growing in my mind right now, right here. The pain that is inevitable, but it is the pain that is incurable. I guess I will have to live with it for the rest of my life. Anyway, I know it sounds crazy when I say that I am afraid of losing you. We are not boyfriend and girlfriend, so I shouldn't feel that way. But I can't lie to myself, nor to you. I am afraid. I am afraid that the day will come.

It's the future I can't change, so I'll accept my fate.

98

Mindset

The older you become, the more thoughtful you are, but in a relationship, no amount of thoughts would be enough to keep problems away. Some problems might happen one way or another. When you deal with them, you should be thoughtful and positive too.

Be that as it may, you should be mindful about the toxic vibes. For example, if your partner has a negative vibe, he or she might spread it to you too. It's infectious, but it's undetectable.

Have a positive mindset, and try to avoid a negative vibe. Try not to react negatively when bad things occur. Especially in a relationship!

You should be calm and deal with your problems in a calmful way. Having said that, if you believe that your relationship problem is unsolvable, you should decide.

To go on or to move on!

It's hard to decide, but sometimes it's better to be realistic about a relationship than passive!

99

Friendship

Friends! Everybody has friends. Good friends. Best friends. Whatever! I did have some friends. Yes, I did, but not anymore. Many of them either left or got removed from the list. Not because they were bad or something. I just don't have enough time for friendship like that. You can call me a weirdo, or you call me anything, and I don't care anymore.

Some friends, in my opinion, are good and bad at the same time. If they are good people, they influence you in a positive way. If they are bad people, you know what you'll get: Bad influence.

My life has been tough enough, and when I can, I avoid as many problems as possible. When people give me problems, I simply run away from them. When they try to invade my personal space, I just have to let them go. I have no choice!

Friendship can be good also, but you need to find good friends.

100

Relationship

A relationship, in many ways, is similar to friendship. It takes courage to start a relationship, and it takes effort to keep it. Both people need to be almost equally committed, or it would fail. I speak from experiences after many guys have come and gone, usually leaving me disappointed. That's why I find it hard to trust anyone easily. I mean, you can't tell between a good guy and a better guy.

A good man usually fades away for one reason: He doesn't think he's good enough for me, so he asks me to break up.

A better man is even harder to find and much more difficult to keep. Many women might find him attractive also. That's when I become indecisive about the future with such a man.

If a relationship is not good for you, you don't need it. It's okay to be alone (again) as long as you're happy. It's okay to love yourself if no one else loves you. Good?

It's Okay.

Don't miss out!

Visit the website below and you can sign up to receive emails whenever Dara Ly publishes a new book. There's no charge and no obligation.

https://books2read.com/r/B-A-HAXZ-VSBNC

Connecting independent readers to independent writers.